What Is for Supper?

¿Qué hay para cenar?

by Deborah Schecter

ISBN: 978-1-338-70276-7
Illustrated by Anne Kennedy

Published by Scholastic Inc., 557 Broadway, New York, NY 10012
10 9 8 7 6 68 23 24 25 26/0
Printed in Jiaxing, China. First printing, June 2020.

SCHOLASTIC

I like pasta.

Me gusta la pasta.

I like pizza.

Me gusta la pizza.

I like tacos.

Me gustan los tacos.

I like grilled cheese.

Me gusta el sándwich
de queso fundido.

I like fish sticks.

Me gustan las barritas
de pescado.

I like rice and beans.

Me gusta el arroz con frijoles.

I like to eat!

¡Me gusta comer!